Ken's cap

Story written by Gill Munton
Illustrated by Tim Archbold

Speed Sounds

Ask your child to say the sounds (not the letter names) clearly and quickly, in and out of order. Make sure he or she does not add 'uh' to the end of the sounds, e.g. 'f' not 'fuh'.

Each box contains one sound. Focus sounds for this story are circled.

Consonants

f	l	m	n	r	s	v	z	sh	**th**	ng
ff	**ll**		nn		ss	ve	zz			nk
							s			

b	c	d	g	h	j	p	qu	t	w	x	y	ch
bb	k		gg			pp		tt	wh			tch
	ck											

Vowels

Ask your child to say the sounds in and out of order.

a	e	i	o	u
at	h**e**n	**i**n	**o**n	**u**p

ay	ee	igh	ow	oo
d**ay**	s**ee**	h**igh**	bl**ow**	z**oo**

Story Green Words

For each word ask your child to read the separate sounds, e.g. 'b-u-s', 'p-oo-l' and then blend sounds together to make the word, e.g. 'bus', 'pool'. Sometimes one sound is represented by more than one letter, e.g. 'th', 'oo'. These are underlined.

Dan Ken tip-up tru<u>ck</u> mud pit ba<u>ck</u>

slop cap hut

Ask your child to read the root first and then the whole word with the suffix.

tip → tips

Red Words

Red words don't sound like they look. Ask your child to read the words but if he or she gets stuck read the word to your child.

the	of	to
no	my	I
said	are	your
you	be	put

Ken's cap

Do not read the story to your child first. Point to the words as your child reads. If your child gets stuck on a word help him or her say the sounds and blend them together.

Re-read each sentence to your child to help him or her remember what he or she has read. Discuss what is happening on each page.

Dan

Ken

Dan is in his tip-up truck.
The tip-up truck is full of mud.

Dan has got to tip the mud in this pit.

Dan tips up the back of the truck.

Slop slop

Yes! The mud is in the pit.

But Ken has lost his cap.

“Is it in the hut?”

“No.”

"Is it in the truck?"

"No."

"It is in the pit!

I left my cap

in that pit!"

Now ask your child to re-read the story helping him or her think about the best way to read each sentence.

Questions to talk about

Read the questions aloud to your child and ask him or her to find the answers on the relevant pages. Do not ask your child to read the questions – the words are harder than he or she can read at the moment.

p.9 Who is standing in the pit while Dan is in the tip-up truck?

p.10 What noise does the mud make when it is going into the pit?

p.11 Where does Dan think the cap could be?

p.12 Where else does Dan think the cap could be?

p.13 Where has Ken left his cap?

Speedy Green Words

Ask your child to read the words clearly and quickly – across the rows, down the columns, and in and out of order.

full	has	lost
his	lost	left
in	that	got
left	is	yes

Read Write Inc.

Phonics

BOOK BAG BOOKS

Ken's cap

Set 2: Purple Storybooks

Use Set 2 Purple Storybooks and Purple Get Writing! Book 2 after learning Speed Sounds Set 1.

OXFORD UNIVERSITY PRESS

www.oup.com

web www.oxfordprimary.com
email primary.enquiries@oup.com
tel +44 (0)1536 452610

Read Write Inc. Phonics
Black and White Storybooks
Purple Set 2:
Mixed Pack of 10
ISBN 9780198372639
Mixed Pack of 100
ISBN 9780198372646

Notes to Parents or Carers

Your child has been reading this book at school. Let your child show you how well he or she can read it.

If your child needs help, follow the advice in the small parent notes next to each activity.

Remember to praise your child's success!

OXFORD
UNIVERSITY PRESS

Great Clarendon Street, Oxford, OX2 6DP, United Kingdom

Oxford University Press is a department of the University of Oxford. It furthers the University's objective of excellence in research, scholarship, and education by publishing worldwide. Oxford is a registered trade mark of Oxford University Press in the UK and in certain other countries

First published by Ruth Miskin Literacy Ltd 2004
This edition published by Oxford University Press 2016

Mixed Pack of 10
ISBN 978-0-19-837263-9

Mixed Pack of 100
ISBN 978-0-19-837264-6

23

Printed in China by Golden Cup

The manufacturer's authorised representative in the EU for product safety is Oxford University Press España S.A. of El Parque Empresarial San Fernando de Henares, Avenida de Castilla, 2 – 28830 Madrid (www.oup.es/en or product.safety@oup.com). OUP España S.A. also acts as importer into Spain of products made by the manufacturer.

Read Write Inc. Phonics

Ken's cap

Set 2 Story 1

a e i o u

Story by Gill Munton
Illustrated by Tim Archbold
Series developed by Ruth Miskin

OXFORD